ASSESSING YOUR CHILD'S PROGRES

Testing and assessment in the National Curriculum

Pupils between the ages of 7 and 11 (Years 3–6) cover Key Stage 2 of the National Curriculum. In May of their final year of Key Stage 2 (Year 6) all pupils take written National Tests (commonly known as SATs) in the three most important subjects: English, Mathematics and Science. Your child may already have taken some National Tests at the end of Key Stage 1 (Year 2). These will have been in number, shape and space, reading, writing, handwriting and spelling.

At the end of Key Stage 1, your child will have been awarded a National Curriculum level for each subject tested. When your child eventually takes the Key Stage 2 tests, he or she again will be awarded a level. On average, pupils are expected to advance one level for every two years they are at school. The target for pupils at the end of Key Stage 1 is Level 2. By the end of Key Stage 2, four years later, the target is Level 4. The table below will show you how your child should progress.

	7 years	11 years
Level 6		Exceptional performance
Level 5		Exceeded targets for age group
Level 4	Exceptional performance	Achieved targets for age group
Level 3	Exceeded targets for age group	Working towards targets for age group
Level 2	Achieved targets for age group	Working towards targets for age group
Level 1	Working towards targets for age group	Working towards targets for age group

Key:
- Exceptional performance
- Exceeded targets for age group
- Achieved targets for age group
- Working towards targets for age group

Assessing your child's progress throughout Key Stage 2 of the National Curriculum

The aim of the Letts Assessment books is to help you monitor your child's progress in English, Mathematics and Science throughout Key Stage 2. There are four books for each subject – one for each year, starting with 7–8 year olds. The questions in the books become progressively harder with each year, so that for 10–11 year olds, the questions will be at a level similar to the Key Stage 2 National Tests.

After completing a book, your child will have a score which you will be able to interpret using the progress indicator provided. This will give you a guide to the level at which your child is working.

ASSESSING YOUR CHILD'S PROGRESS

Using this book to assess your child's progress in Mathematics

This book is for 8–9 year olds (Year 4). It contains four basic features:

Questions: 40 questions, arranged in order of level of difficulty as follows:
10 at Level 2 (pages 1–8)
15 at Level 3 (pages 9–21)
15 at Level 4 (pages 22–35)

Answers: showing acceptable responses and marks

Note to Parent: giving advice on what your child should be doing and how to help

Progress Chart: showing you how to interpret your child's marks to arrive at a level

- Your child should not attempt to do all the questions in the book in one go. Try setting ten questions at a time. If your child does not understand a question, you might want to explain it. Although the questions in this book are not meant to constitute a formal test, you should encourage your child to answer as many as possible without help. Read the questions to your child if you think it will help.
- When your child has completed the questions, turn to the Answer section at the back of the book. Using the recommended answers, award your child the appropriate mark or marks for each question. In the margin of each question page, there are small boxes. These are divided in half with the marks available for that question at the bottom, and a blank at the top for you to fill in your child's score.
- Collate your child's marks on the grid on page 46. Then add them up. Once you have the total, turn to page 36 at the front of the Answer section and look at the Progress Chart to determine your child's level.
- Work through the answers with your child, using the Note to Parent to help give advice, correct mistakes and explain problems.

Equipment your child will need for this book

The following equipment may be needed for answering these questions:

- a pen, pencil, rubber and coloured pencils
- a ruler (30 cm plastic ruler is most suitable)
- a calculator. An inexpensive four-function calculator is all that is required. Do not let your child use a scientific calculator which has too many complicated functions
- a mirror and tracing paper. These are useful for symmetry questions

Some questions in this book ban the use of a calculator.

The following symbol is used: 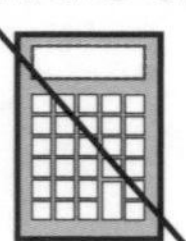

MARKS

1 Here are six numbers.

43 62 17 84 93 27

a How many tens are there in 43?

....

1 Q1a

b How many units are there in 84?

....

1 Q1b

c Write the six numbers in order, starting with the largest one first.

....

1 Q1c

2 The 28 children in Class 3 each write down what their favourite biscuit is.

Here are their answers:

ginger	3
chocolate	9
digestive	7
shortbread	5
rich tea	4

Draw a block graph to show this.

5

Q2

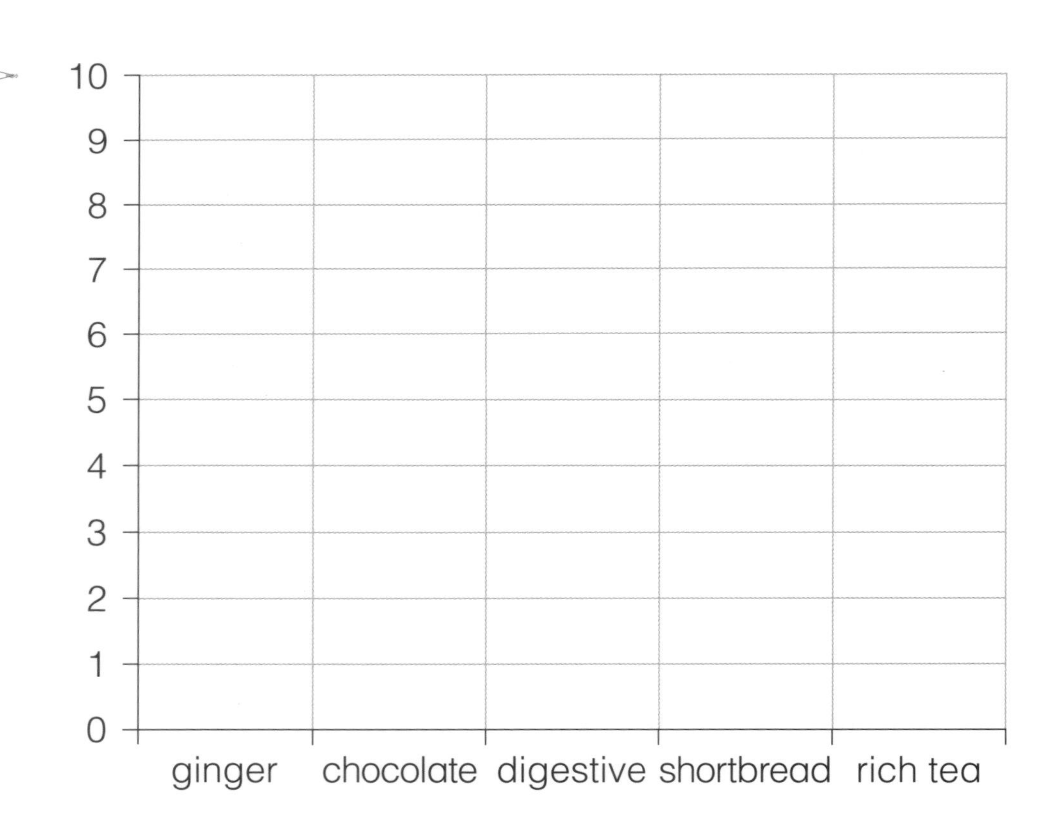

3 Jane has four number cards.

1	2	3	4

She also has an add card [+]

and a subtract card [–].

She makes sums with two of the number cards and either an add card or a subtract card.

Write down **two** different sums she could make with an **even** answer, and **two** with an **odd** answer. Write the numbers in the boxes.

[ ] [ ] [ ] = [ ] even

[ ] [ ] [ ] = [ ] even

[ ] [ ] [ ] = [ ] odd

[ ] [ ] [ ] = [ ] odd

4

Q3

4 Q4

4 Draw lines to show which box you would put each object in. Two have been done for you.

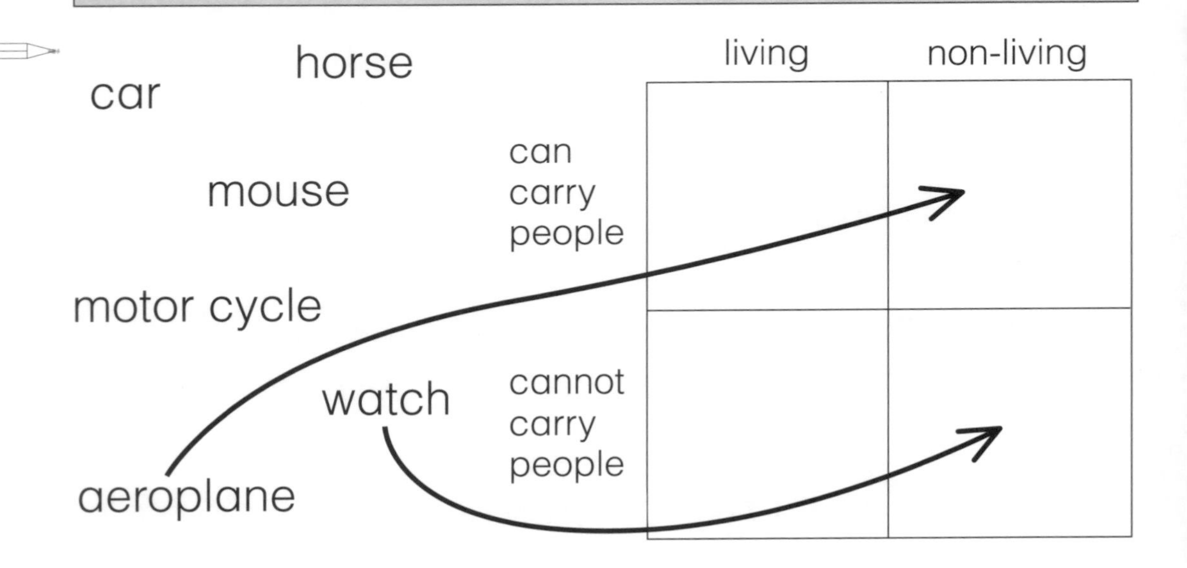

5 Tom, Dick and Harry go fishing.
Tom catches 14 fish.
Dick catches 3 more fish than Tom.
Harry catches 5 fish less than Tom.

1 Q5a

a How many fish does Dick catch?

....

1 Q5b

b How many fish does Harry catch?

....

MARKS

6 Here is a number grid.

1	2	3	4	5	6	7	8	9	10
11	12	13	14	15	16	17	18	19	20
21	22	23	24	25	26	27	28	29	30
31	32	33	34	35	36	37	38	39	40

a Fill in the missing numbers in this track.

3 Q6a

2			
12			
			25

b Fill in the missing numbers in this track.

2 Q6b

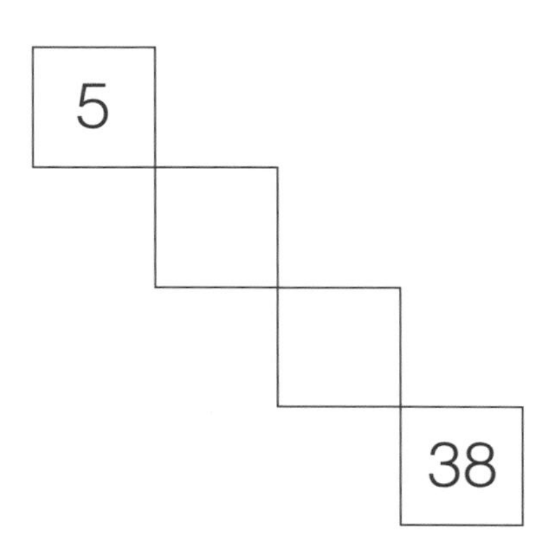

7 Here are some shapes. They are triangles, circles, squares, pentagons, rectangles and hexagons.

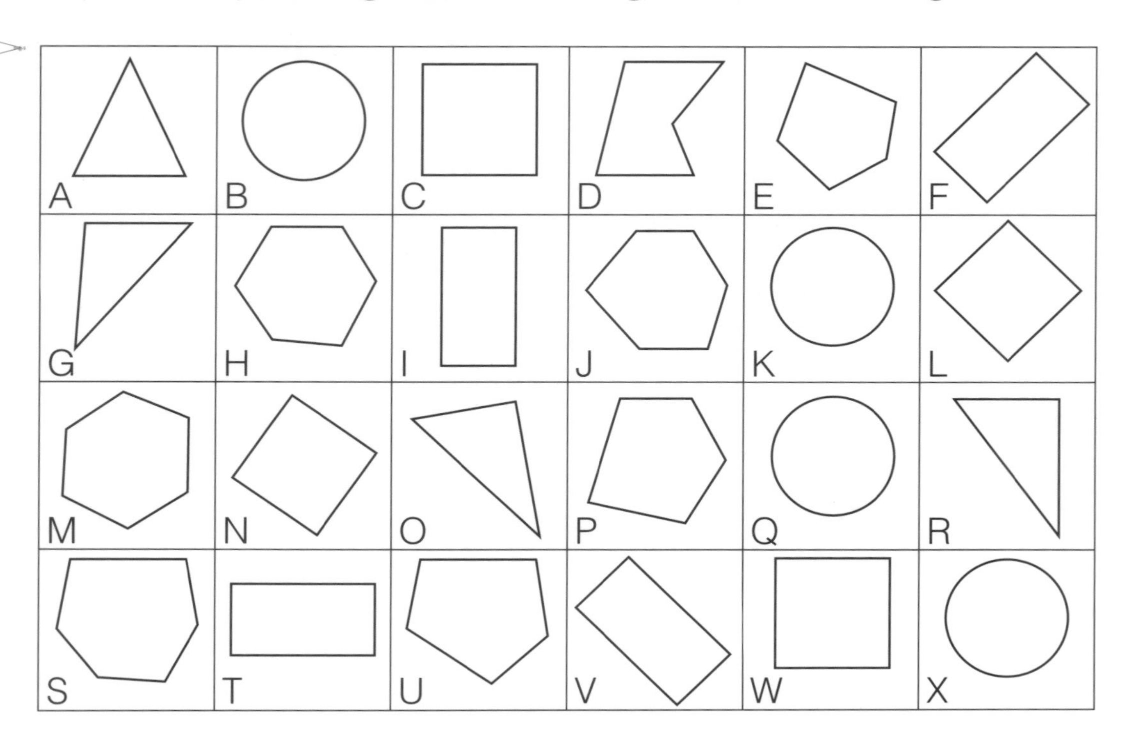

a How many triangles are there?

1 Q7a

b How many pentagons are there?

1 Q7b

c Shade in **two** different shapes which have at least two right angles in them.

2 Q7c

MARKS

8 Alice makes a right angle by folding a piece of paper.

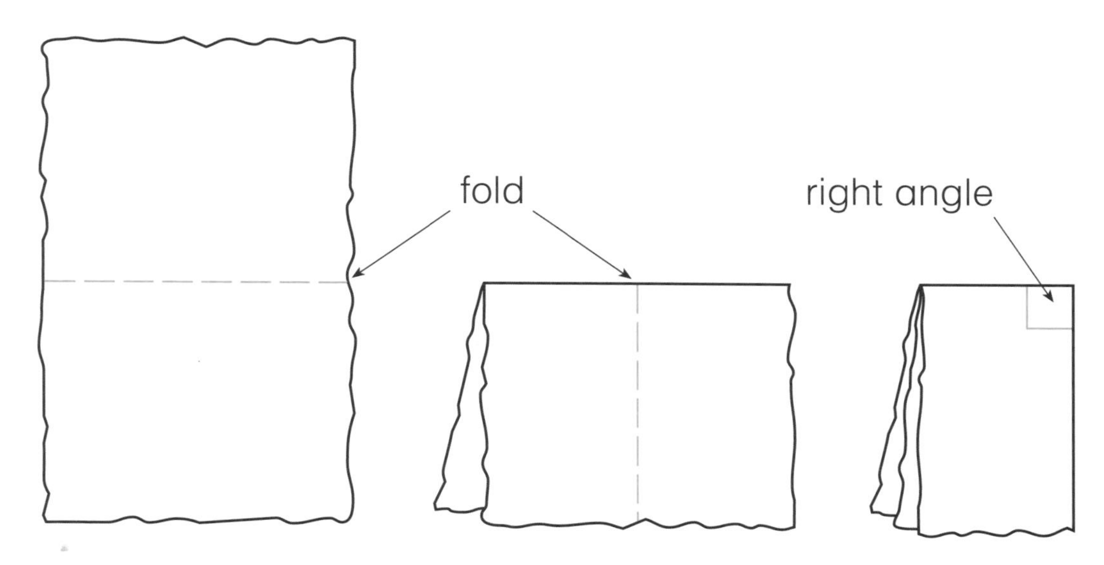

She then uses it to test for right angles in the shapes shown below.

Mark all the right angles that you can find. One has been done for you.

5

Q8

9 Here are a square and a triangle.

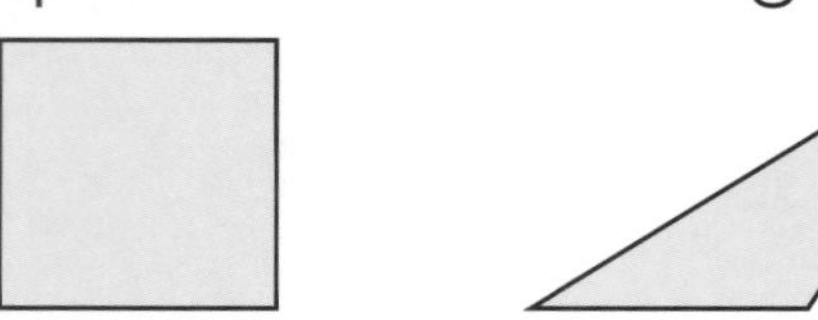

Write down two differences between these two shapes.

1 ....

2 ....

2 Q9

10 Nigel's mum made him a cake for his tenth birthday. The cake was cut into ten sections.

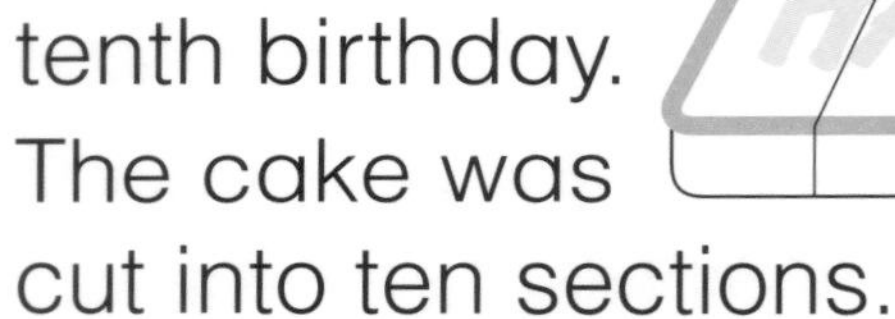

Nigel shared his cake with Stuart and gave him half.

a How many pieces did he give to Stuart?

....

1 Q10a

b What fraction did Nigel have left?

....

1 Q10b

11 Here are three number cards.

2	5	7

One number that can be made with the three cards is:

5	2	7

a **What is the largest number you can make?**

1 Q11a

b **What is the smallest number you can make?**

1 Q11b

c **What is the difference between them?**

1 Q11c

12 This question asks you to make approximations.

a Write 570 to the nearest 100.

....

1 Q12a

b Write 907 to the nearest 100.

....

1 Q12b

c Write 460 to the nearest 50.

....

1 Q12c

d Write 333 to the nearest 50.

....

1 Q12d

13 Emma had £5.00. With it she bought two bunches of flowers.

How much change did she get?

£ ....

1 Q13

MARKS

14 These are the names of some measures.

centimetres **metres** **kilograms**
grams **kilometres**

Choose a word from the list to show what you would use to measure:

5
Q14

a The height of a house.

 ....

b The width of a book.

....

c The weight of an elephant.

....

d The weight of an apple.

....

e The distance from London to Paris.

....

15 Some children listed the contents of their school desks.

	pencils	books	rulers	felt pens
Jane	1	4	0	10
Emma	2	1	1	3
David	2	3	0	9
Sam	3	2	1	5

a Who had the most felt pens?

1 Q15a

....

b Who had the least books?

1 Q15b

....

c How many pencils do the children own altogether?

1 Q15c

....

d How many objects are there in David's desk?

1 Q15d

....

MARKS

16 Asif and Tanya visit a fairground.

Roundabout 80p a ride

Helter Skelter £1.25 a go

a Asif has **two** rides on the roundabout. How much does it cost him?

....

1 Q16a

b Tanya has **three** goes on the helter skelter. How much does it cost her?

....

1 Q16b

c Tanya and Asif both have a lucky dip. Tanya pays for both of them with a £1 coin. How much change should she get?

....

1 Q16c

17 Fill in the boxes to make these sums correct.

a $3 \times \square = 15$

b $2 \times \square = 20$

c $\square \times 4 = 20$

d $\square \times \square = 25$

both numbers the same

e $\square \times 5 = 50$

f $\square \times 2 = 4$

6
Q17

MARKS

18 Here is a graph showing the highest temperature each day during one week.

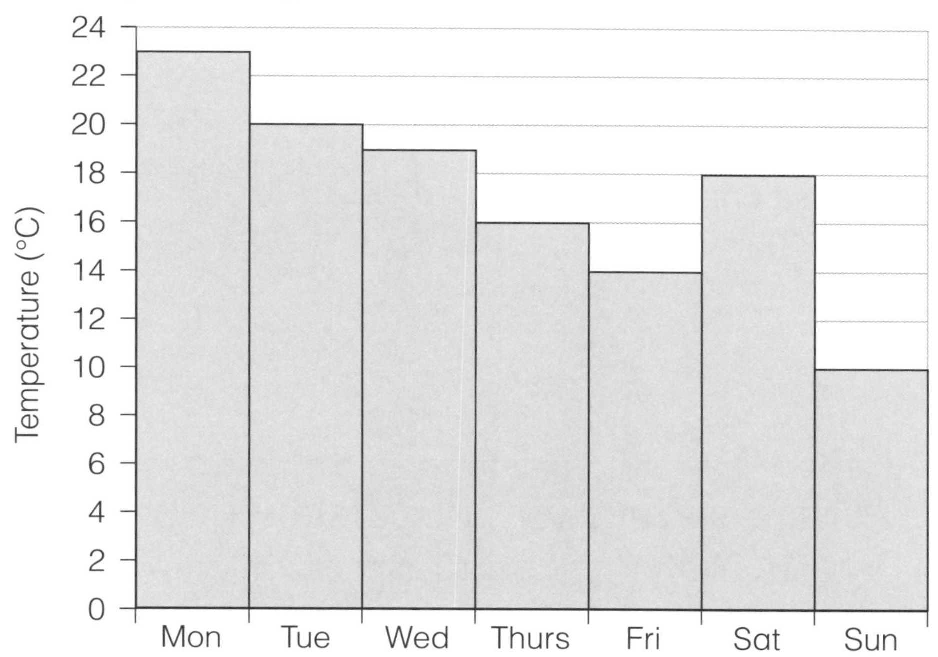

a

Put a tick ✓ or a cross ✗ in each box to show whether you think these statements are true or false.

2
Q18a

The start of the week was colder than the end of the week.

Saturday was colder than Wednesday.

b

What was the temperature on Thursday?

Q18b

.... °C

19 Tom is sorting shapes.

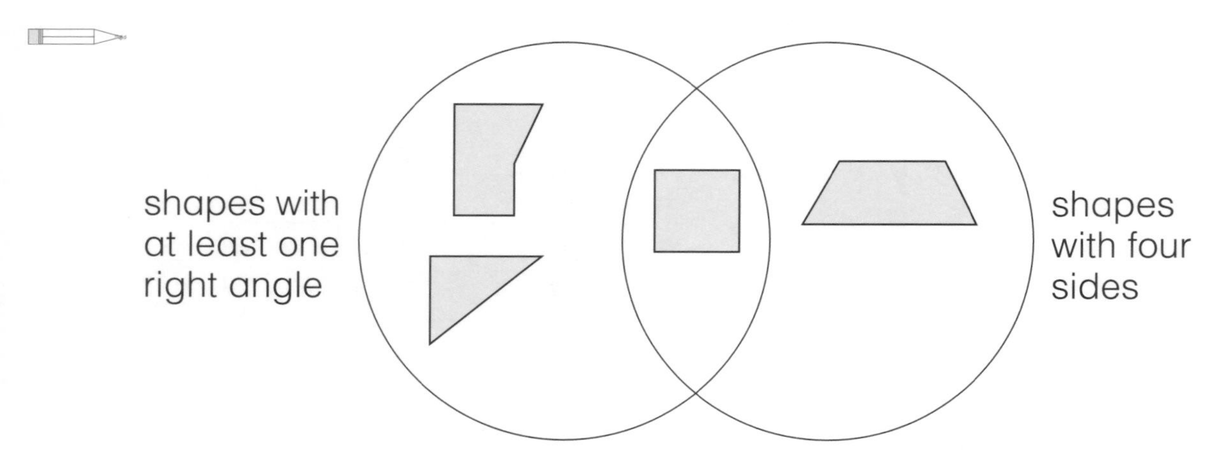

Where should Tom put these shapes? Write the letters in the correct part of the circles.

2
Q19

20 Put each of these lists of numbers into the correct order, starting with the smallest first.

a 6 10 18 12 14 4 20 16 2 8

....

b 35 5 25 20 45 10 30 15 40

....

2
Q20

MARKS

21 Julie and Brian have to travel to their new home.
It is 12 km away.

They fill their van with furniture and make **three** trips to their new home and back to their old home.

a How far do they travel altogether?

....

1
Q21a

The van travels 4 km on 1 litre of petrol.

b How many litres of petrol will they need to buy?

....

1
Q21b

22 The children in Brookdale School were asked what pets they had. There were 150 children.

Jenny drew a pictogram to show the results. She used these drawings:

cats  represents 10 cats

dogs  represents 10 dogs

fish  represents 10 fish

Complete the pictogram for Jenny.

3
Q22

		total
cats		
dogs		30
fish		25

MARKS

23 Susan drew some shapes on squared paper.

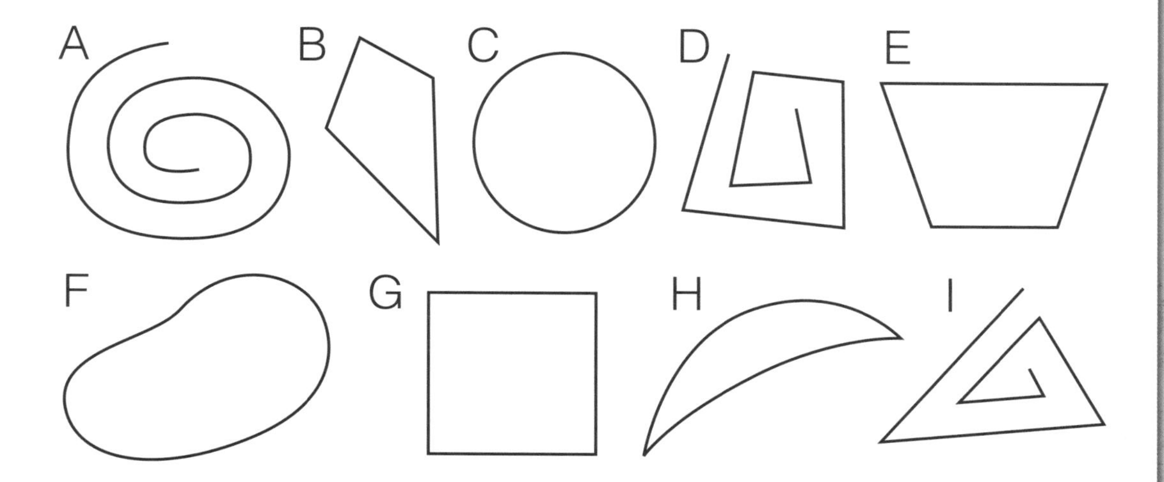

a Sort these shapes into **three** groups.

2
Q23a

group 1 ....

group 2 ....

group 3 ....

b Describe how you have grouped them.

Q23b

....

....

....

24 The map shows the approximate distance in kilometres of certain cities from London.

a Which city on the map is the greatest distance from London?

....

1
Q24a

b Which city is the shortest distance from London?

....

1
Q24b

MARKS

c

How many kilometres would you travel on a return journey to:

2
Q24c

Belfast ....

Southampton ....

d

Which is the greater distance in kilometres from London?

4
Q24d

Glasgow or Edinburgh .... by .... km

Newcastle or Belfast .... by .... km

25

Tick ✓ the box below each shape if you think it has **reflection symmetry**. Put a cross ✗ in the box if it has not got reflection symmetry.

5
Q25

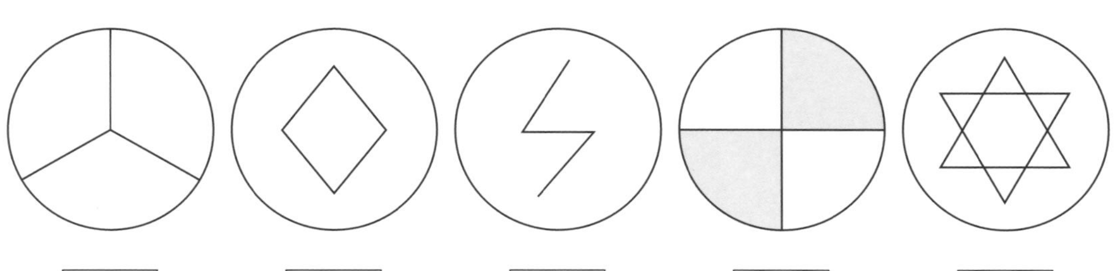

A ☐ B ☐ C ☐ D ☐ E ☐

QUESTIONS LEVEL 4

26 Josh and Jethro like to collect car numbers. They made a list of their car numbers and decided to round them up or down to the nearest ten like this:

units 1–4 down to 0

units 5–9 up to the next 10

10
Q26

Help Josh and Jethro to finish rounding their numbers to the nearest ten.

Josh's			Jethro's		
741	→	740	389	→	390
362	→		411	→	
419	→		277	→	
328	→		891	→	
517	→		909	→	
696	→		899	→	

MARKS

27 Four packs of cards cost £1.80.
A packet of five glue sticks costs £4.

£4

a What is the cost of **one** pack of cards?

....

1
Q27a

b What is the cost of **one** glue stick?

....

1
Q27b

c If 27 children each need one glue stick, how many packets do I need to buy?

....

1
Q27c

d How many glue sticks are left over?

....

1
Q27d

28 Carl and Alec have pieced together a shapes jigsaw. One piece is missing. Here is the incomplete puzzle:

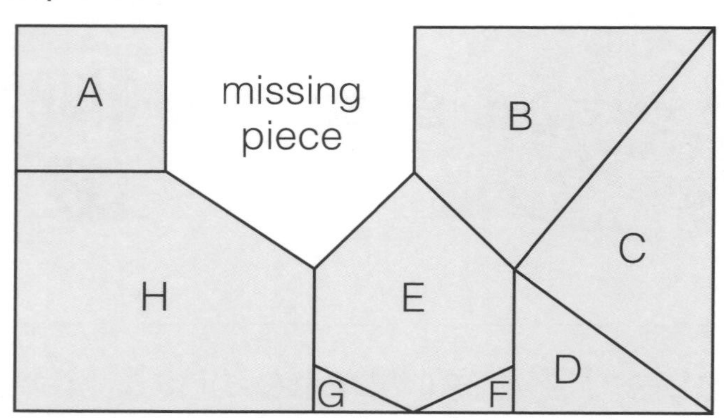

a How many quadrilaterals are there?

....

1 Q28a

b Which shape is a hexagon?

....

1 Q28b

c Which shape is a regular shape? What is its name?

....

1 Q28c

d Name the missing shape.

....

1 Q28d

MARKS

e

Which shapes are triangles?

1
Q28e

....

f

What is special about G and F?

1
Q28f

....

29 Mary buys packets of sweets with 100 sweets in each packet.

She has a box with 24 packets in it.

a

How many sweets does she have altogether?

1
Q29a

....

She puts ten sweets into paper bags to sell at the school fair.

b

How many paper bags will she need?

1
Q29b

....

5
Q30

30 Tick ✓ **one** box to show how likely you are to:

		impossible	unlikely	likely	certain
a	find a coin in the road tomorrow	☐	☐	☐	☐
b	go to Mars next week	☐	☐	☐	☐
c	not get a six when you roll a dice	☐	☐	☐	☐
d	get a head if you toss a coin	☐	☐	☐	☐
e	see that it is dark tonight	☐	☐	☐	☐

2
Q31

31 What do these machines do?

a

IN

30 24 16 15 9

OUT

36 30 22 21 15

....

b

IN

87 74 56 41 32

OUT

77 64 46 31 22

....

MARKS

32 Jim took part in a sponsored race. Here is part of his sponsor sheet.

Brookdale School Sponsor Sheet

Name of pupil .... Jim Stoker

Class ...4H... Laps completed ...9...

sponsor	amount per lap	amount collected
Mrs Stokes	10p	
Mr Stokes	5p	
M. Binns	3p	
Mr Moore		54p

a Complete the **amount collected** column in the top part of the sheet.

3
Q32a

b Mr Moore gave Jim 54p. How much per lap did he sponsor Jim for?

....

1
Q32b

c If Jim had only completed eight laps, how much would Mr Stokes have paid him?

....

1
Q32c

33 Here are three cars.

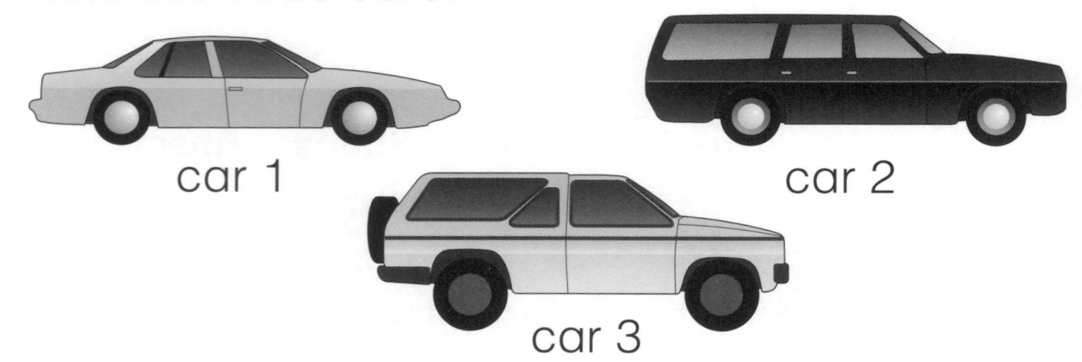

Car 1 travels 12 km on 1 litre of petrol.

a How far will it travel on 8 litres of petrol?

....

1 Q33a

Car 2 travels 270 km on 10 litres of petrol.

b How many kilometres per litre did it do?

....

1 Q33b

Car 3 travelled 42 km further than Car 2.

c How many kilometres did it go?

....

1 Q33c

MARKS

34 Tom is making shapes out of sticky paper. He uses squares and triangles.

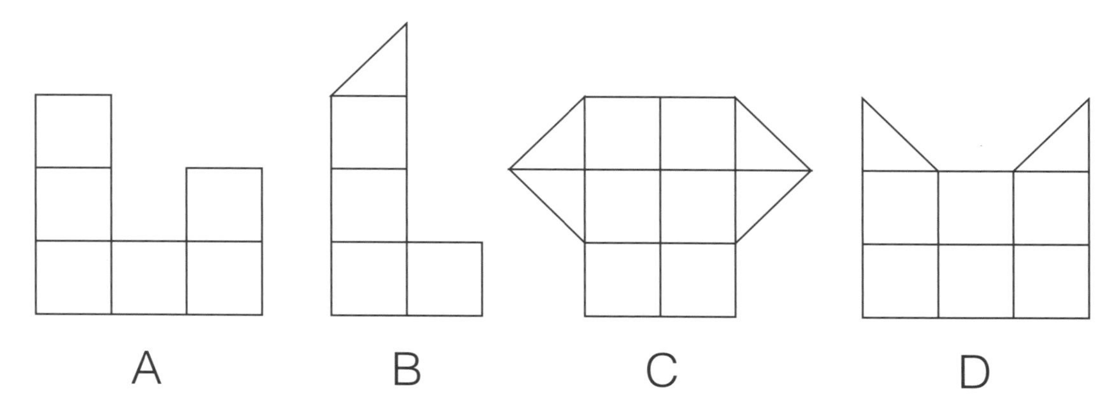

a Which shape has the largest area?

....

1 Q34a

b What is the area of shape D?

....

1 Q34b

c Draw **two** different shapes which both have areas of $8\frac{1}{2}$ squares on the grids below.

2 Q34c

35 Below are some points on a grid showing the different distances a cyclist travelled at different times during a race.

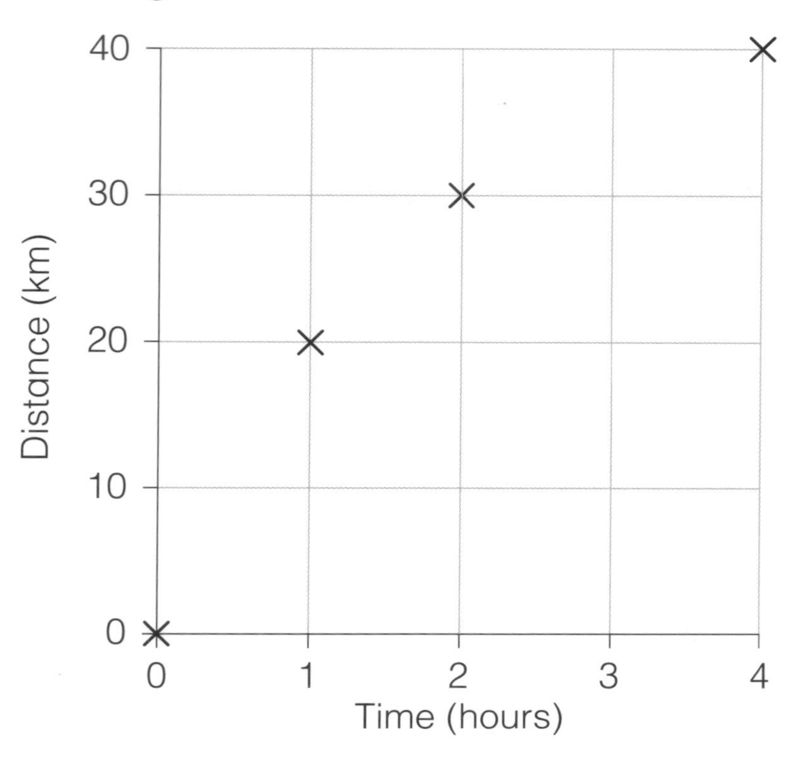

a After three hours the cyclist had cycled 35 km. Mark this with a cross **X** on the graph.

1
Q35a

b Use a ruler to join all five crosses with a line.

1
Q35b

c How far had the cyclist travelled after $1\frac{1}{2}$ hours?

1
Q35c

....

MARKS

36 The following shapes are only half complete. The dotted lines show lines of symmetry.

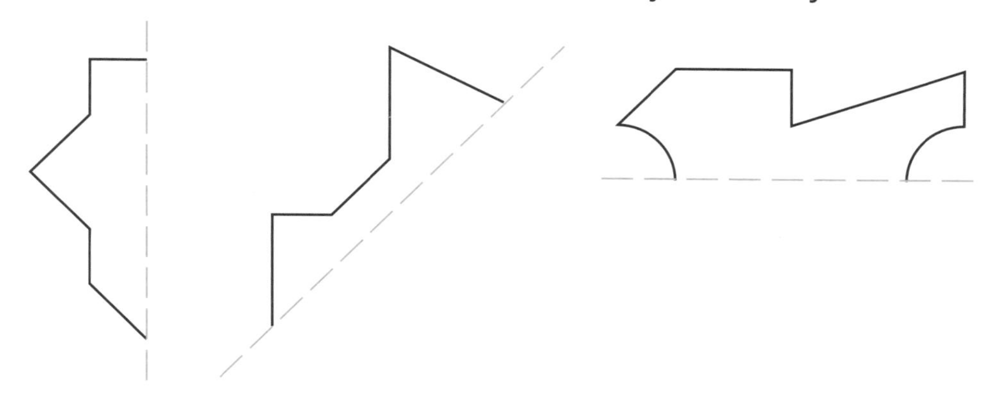

Complete the shapes using the lines of symmetry shown.

3 Q36

37 Colour in the fraction shown on each drawing.

4 Q37

a

$\frac{1}{8}$

b

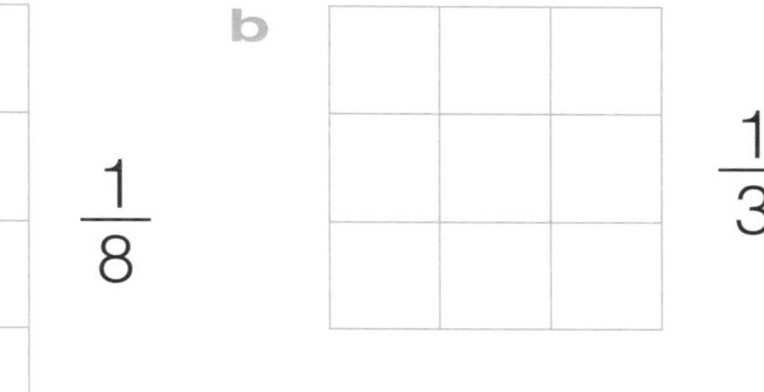

$\frac{1}{3}$

c

$\frac{1}{4}$

d

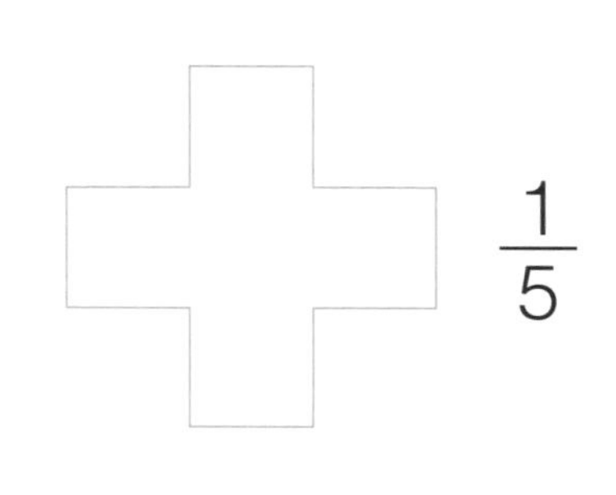

$\frac{1}{5}$

LEVEL 4

MARKS

38 Class 6 did a survey about pocket money. These are their answers.

50p	£1.20	75p	60p	£1.40
80p	£1.70	65p	£1.50	£1.25
40p	£1.45	£1.15	£1.60	90p

Complete the frequency table below.

9

Q38

money	frequency	total
0–19p		
20–39p		
40–59p		
60–79p		
80–99p		
£1.00–£1.19		
£1.20–£1.39		
£1.40–£1.59		
£1.60–£1.79		

LEVEL 4

MARKS

39 This graph shows the profits made by the Leafy Valley Steam Railway in one year.

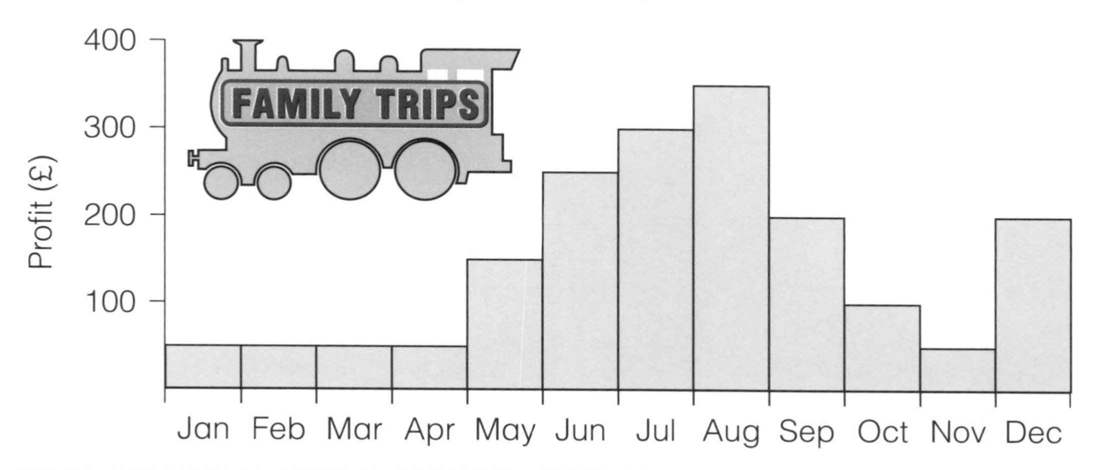

a Which was the railway's most successful month?

1 Q39a

b Why do you think it was the most successful?

1 Q39b

c How much money was made during the three most successful months?

1 Q39c

d Why do you think December was more successful than other winter months?

1 Q39d

40

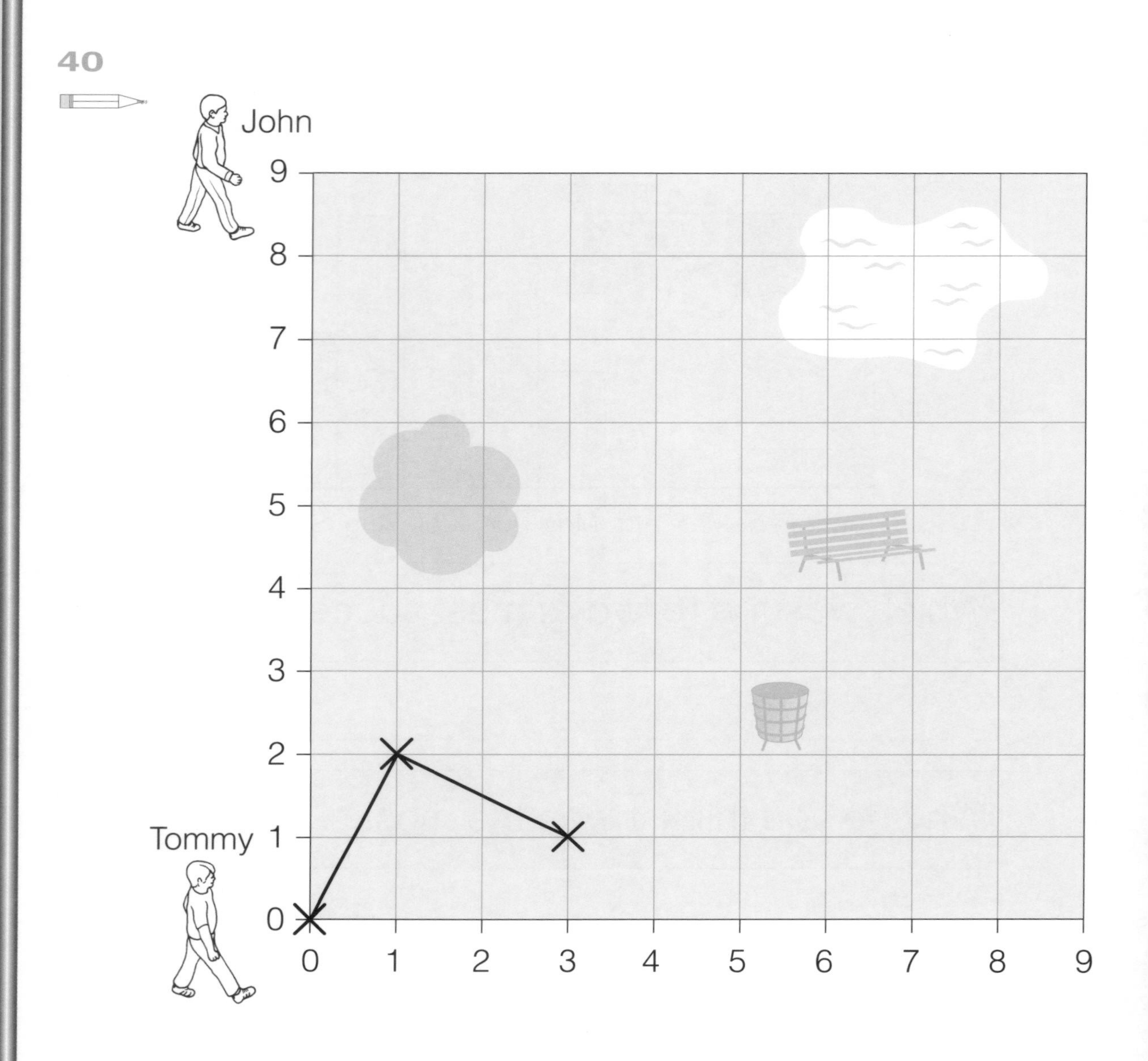

Tommy and John are looking for buried treasure.

Tommy set out from (0,0) and followed this course:
(0,0) (1,2) (3,1) (5,5) (7,6) (8,1) (0,0)

John set out from (0,9) and followed this course:
(0,9) (3,5) (5,7) (4,4) (4,2) (6,1) (0,0)

They both walked over the treasure.

MARKS

What is the point where the treasure can be found? Tommy's journey has been started for you. Mark the points of each journey and join them up with straight lines.

2

Q40

The treasure can be found at:

....

MARKING YOUR CHILD'S QUESTIONS

- The answers given here are correct answers. They are the answers the question-setter expects. When marking your child's questions, you must look at your child's answers and judge whether they deserve credit. Award the mark if the answer deserves credit.
- At this age, your child's spelling may show a number of errors. Do not mark any answer wrong because the words are misspelt. Read the word aloud and if it sounds correct award the mark. For example, 'ekwul' would be acceptable for 'equal'.
- When you go through the questions with your child, try to be positive. Look for good things that have been done in addition to showing where errors have been made.
- Enter your child's marks on the grid on page 46, and then refer to the chart below to determine your child's level.

Progress Chart

Total marks scored	Progress made	Suggested action
50 or below	Your child is still working at Level 2.	Try to identify difficulties in the early questions, particularly the first ten. Work through them with your child and use the notes to help.
51–90	Your child is working with increasing confidence within Level 3.	Again try to identify where errors are occurring. Practise money calculations, largest and smallest etc. and talk about shapes.
91–120	Your child is reasonably confident with the Level 3 work in this book and is starting to work within the early stages of Level 4.	Practise questions involving place value and multiplying by 10 and 100, the multiplication tables up to 10×10 and questions involving addition, subtraction and division.
121–140	Your child is confident with the Level 4 work presented here.	Give your child extra practice, especially with questions involving graphs and tables.
141 and above	Your child is making rapid progress. This is an excellent score.	Congratulate your child. Make sure your child is confident with the mental recall of multiplication tables up to 10×10.

- A child at the end of Year 4 (8–9 year olds) should be, of the above statements, at about the third statement.

ANSWERS

1 a 4 — *1 mark*
b 4 — *1 mark*
c 93, 84, 62, 43, 27, 17 — *1 mark*

Note to Parent

Using a tens and units board (or sheet) may help.

Tens	Units

Total 3 marks

2

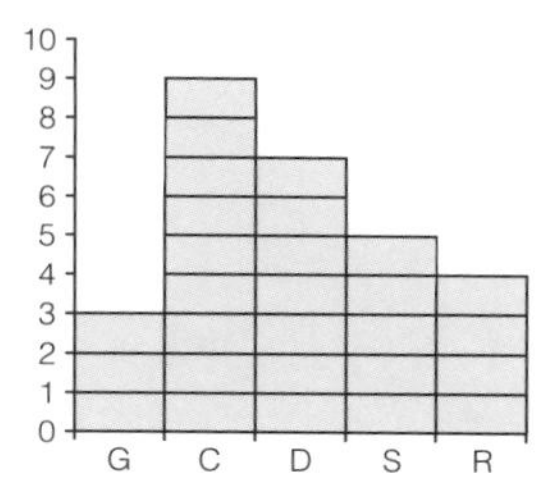

Award one mark for each correctly drawn column — *5 marks*

Note to Parent

A block graph has columns made up of individual blocks. If the individual blocks were not drawn, it would be a bar chart or bar graph.

Total 5 marks

3 Check your child's work; two correct sums with even answers — *1 mark each*
and two correct sums with odd answers — *1 mark each*

Note to Parent

Even numbers are made by adding or subtracting two even or two odd numbers. Use numbers on cards, and objects if necessary, to help.

Total 4 marks

4

	living	non-living
can carry people	horse	car motor cycle aeroplane
cannot carry people	mouse	watch

Award one mark for each correct answer — *4 marks*

Note to Parent

Sorting objects by various criteria is an important skill that needs practising.

Total 4 marks

5 a 17 — *1 mark*
b 9 — *1 mark*

Note to Parent

Use counters to help if necessary, but encourage your child to work the answer out mentally if he or she can, and to check with the calculator.

Total 2 marks

6 a

2			
12	13	14	15
			25

b

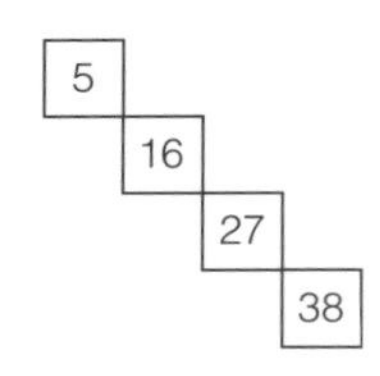

Award one mark for each correct number — *5 marks*

Note to Parent

Let your child follow the line of the track on the grid with her or his finger if needed.

Total 5 marks

7 a 4 — *1 mark*
b 4 — *1 mark*
c Any two of C, F, I, L, N, T, V, W — *2 marks*

Note to Parent

Try to get your child to identify all the shapes.

Total 4 marks

8

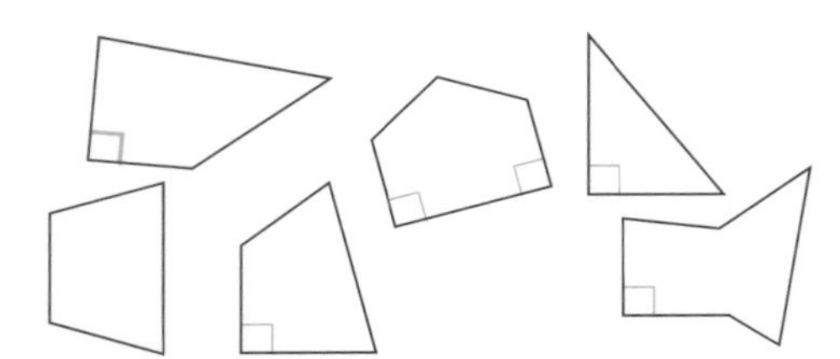

Award one mark for each correct right angle — *5 marks*

Note to Parent

Folding paper to make a right angle is a useful angle measurement activity prior to the introduction of a protractor (which is often a difficult instrument to come to terms with for young children). It is also important for children to recognise right angles in shapes which display other orientations than the usual vertical or horizontal.

Total 5 marks

9 The answers could include any of the following properties:
square: four sides, all sides equal, opposite sides are parallel, angles are right angles
triangle: three sides, all sides different, no right angles, two angles less than a right angle, one angle greater than a right angle
Award one mark for a reference to a difference in sides and one mark for a reference to different angles — *2 marks*

Note to Parent

Try to get your child to describe the properties of other shapes. You could also perhaps draw a right-angled triangle and ask your child to compare the differences again.

Total 2 marks

10 a 5 *1 mark*
b ½ or a half *1 mark*

Note to Parent

Children need to be able to recognise halves and quarters. Finding half a group of ten children, or a quarter of eight sweets, are the sort of questions that can be asked as practice. Use ten cubes or counters and split them into two equal groups.

Total 2 marks

11 a 752 *1 mark*
b 257 *1 mark*
c 495 *1 mark*

Note to Parent

Use number cards if necessary to help your child. A calculator may be used to answer part **c**.

Total 3 marks

12 a 600 *1 mark*
b 900 *1 mark*
c 450 *1 mark*
d 350 *1 mark*

Note to Parent

Children need to be able to give approximate values for answers to calculations. This question assesses your child's ability to round up or down as a first step in the process.

Total 4 marks

13 £2.40 *1 mark*

Note to Parent

Although your child may use a calculator, encourage her or him to find the answer mentally.

Total 1 mark

14 a metres *1 mark*
b centimetres *1 mark*
c kilograms *1 mark*
d grams *1 mark*
e kilometres *1 mark*

Note to Parent

It would be useful to ask your child about measuring other objects. Sometimes the units will be obvious, but for others there could be equally acceptable alternatives, such as the height of a person could be 165 cm or 1.65 m.

Total 5 marks

15	a	Jane	*1 mark*
	b	Emma	*1 mark*
	c	8	*1 mark*
	d	14	*1 mark*

Note to Parent

Children need to be able to read values off tables and charts.

Total 4 marks

16	a	£1.60	*1 mark*
	b	£3.75	*1 mark*
	c	60p	*1 mark*

Note to Parent

Try to encourage your child to work these out mentally. Use real money to help if necessary.

Total 3 marks

17	a	5	*1 mark*
	b	10	*1 mark*
	c	5	*1 mark*
	d	5 × 5	*1 mark*
	e	10	*1 mark*
	f	2	*1 mark*

Note to Parent

Your child should know the 2, 5 and 10 times tables. This question aims to test that.

Total 6 marks

18	a	cross, tick	*1 mark each*
	b	16°C	*1 mark*

Note to Parent

In this question the children are being asked to consider some general interpretations of this fairly straight forward graph.

Total 3 marks

19	A should be placed in the right hand circle	*1 mark*
	B should be placed in the overlapping part with the square	*1 mark*

Note to Parent

The middle part, or intersection, is where shapes that have both properties belong.

Total 2 marks

20	a	2, 4, 6, 8, 10, 12, 14, 16, 18, 20	*1 mark*
	b	5, 10, 15, 20, 25, 30, 35, 40, 45	*1 mark*

Note to Parent

These are number sequences, but jumbled up. Use a number line or a tape measure marked in centimetres to help.

Total 2 marks

21 a 72 km *1 mark*
b 18 litres *1 mark*

Note to Parent

Children often miss key words in questions. Here they are 'and back', so the distance there and back is 24 km. Use your child's answer in part **a** for part **b**.

Total 2 marks

22 55 cats *1 mark*
three dogs *1 mark*
two and a half fish *1 mark*

Note to Parent

Accurate copying of the symbols is not required, but a good indication of half a fish is.

Total 3 marks

23 One example would be:
a Group 1 A, D, I
Group 2 C, F, H
Group 3 B, E, G *2 marks*
b Group 1 are all spiral shapes
Group 2 all have curved edges
Group 3 all have straight edges *2 marks*
The groupings given here can be in any order. Other grouping features could include shapes with four straight edges and shapes which are open.

Note to Parent

The grouping of shapes on the basis of geometrical features is fundamental to much of the work in the topic on shape and space. Children should develop their recognition of basic differences and similarities between shapes and be able to express these features using appropriate language, for example using terms such as edge, sides, straight, curved, closed and sharp-angled.

Total 4 marks

24 a Glasgow *1 mark*
b Southampton *1 mark*
c 1018 km *1 mark*
214 km *1 mark*
d Glasgow by 32 km *2 marks*
Belfast by 94 km *2 marks*
Total 8 marks

25 Ticks: A, B, D, E
Crosses: C
Award one mark for each correct tick or cross *5 marks*

Note to Parent

At this level children should be able to recognise reflection symmetry. Let your child use a mirror to help.

Total 5 marks

26 Josh: 360, 420, 330, 520, 700 — *1 mark each*
Jethro: 410, 280, 890, 910, 900 — *1 mark each*

Note to Parent

Remind your child that numbers below 5 go back to 0, and the numbers 5 and above will go up to 10.

Total 10 marks

27

a	45p	*1 mark*
b	80p	*1 mark*
c	6	*1 mark*
d	3	*1 mark*

Note to Parent

Parts **a** and **b** involve division or sharing equally. Any method can be used as a calculator is not allowed.

Total 4 marks

28

a	2 (shapes A and B)	*1 mark*
b	E	*1 mark*
c	A is regular. It is a square	*1 mark*
d	a pentagon	*1 mark*
e	C, D, G and F	*1 mark*
f	G and F are congruent. Accept a description that they are exactly alike in size and angle, the only difference is position. F is a reflection of G and vice versa.	*1 mark*

Note to Parent

The handling of shapes in the form of puzzles or pictures often leads to an increased awareness of their properties and attributes. A regular shape has all its sides and angles equal.

Total 6 marks

29

a	2400	*1 mark*
b	240	*1 mark*

Note to Parent

This question tests your child's ability to multiply by 100 and divide by 10. Try to get your child to work out the answers mentally (or using pencil and paper) and then to check using a calculator.

Total 2 marks

30

a	Could be any answer supported by reasons, but the expected answer is 'unlikely'	*1 mark*
b	'impossible'	*1 mark*
c & d	Either 'likely' or 'unlikely' are acceptable. 'Impossible' and 'certain' are not valid answers	*1 mark each*
e	'certain' – it will be dark tonight, but the response may be different – your child may not see	*1 mark*

Note to Parent

Ask your child for reasons for his or her answers and discuss the responses.

Total 5 marks

31 a This machine adds 6 — *1 mark*
b This machine subtracts 10 — *1 mark*

Note to Parent

This page gives your child practice in number work. Your child will need to recognise the pattern between the input numbers and the corresponding output numbers.

Total 2 marks

32 a 90p, 45p, 27p — *1 mark each*
b 6p — *1 mark*
c 40p — *1 mark*

Note to Parent

Part **a** is straight forward, involving multiplication by 9. Part **b** involves division by 9.

Total 5 marks

33 a 96 km — *1 mark*
b 27 km — *1 mark*
c 312 km — *1 mark*

Note to Parent

This question uses the basic rules of multiplication and division. Your child may need some help with the meaning of 'kilometres per litre' in part **b**.

Total 3 marks

34 a C — *1 mark*
b 7 squares — *1 mark*
c There are many possibilities. The inclusion of ¼ squares is also acceptable.
Two possible examples are shown below

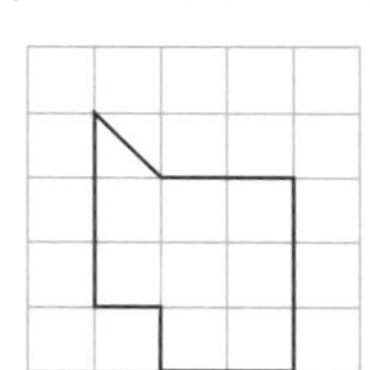

1 mark each

Note to Parent

Area is a property of flat surfaces. This question involves comparison of square and triangular regions for size. Just as children begin to appreciate the need for standard units when measuring length, a similar development is required for area measurement. The concept of a square unit should develop from work where children try to cover surfaces using other shapes, many of which will leave gaps (that is, they will not tessellate).

Total 4 marks

35

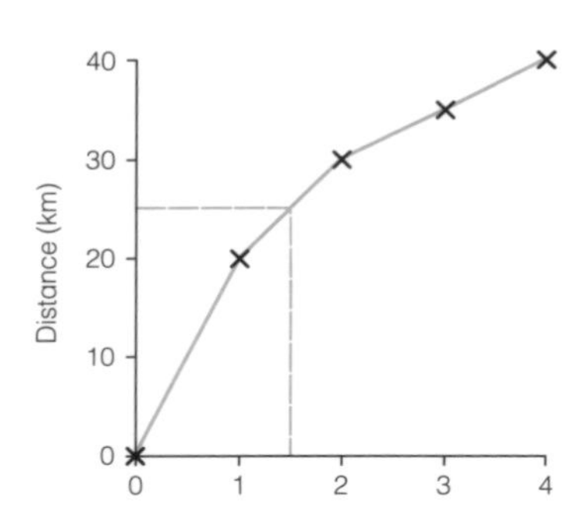

a	Check your child has correctly positioned the cross	*1 mark*
b	A single line clearly linking all five crosses	*1 mark*
c	25 km	*1 mark*

Note to Parent

Points need to be plotted carefully, otherwise graphs will give inaccurate results.

Total 3 marks

36

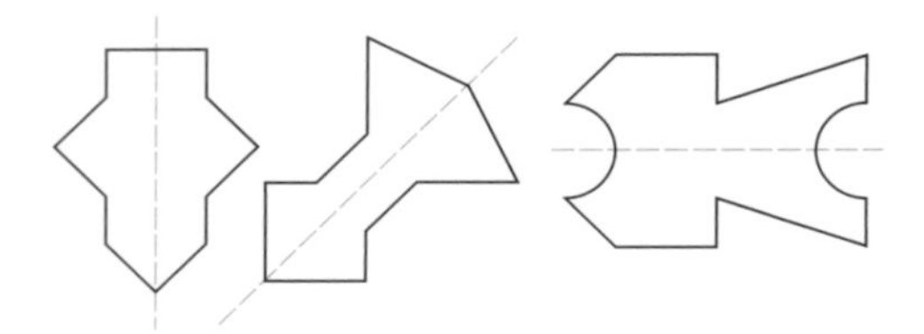

1 mark each

Note to Parent

This question involves the exploration of reflective (line) symmetry. A mirror will make the task much easier and its use is encouraged in the classroom and is also available under test conditions. Children often find lines, or axes, of symmetry in plane shapes practically this way. If a plane shape does not change after reflection, it is said to possess line symmetry.

Total 3 marks

37

a

b

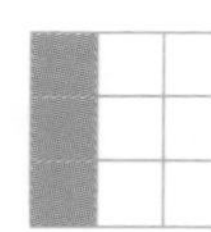

c

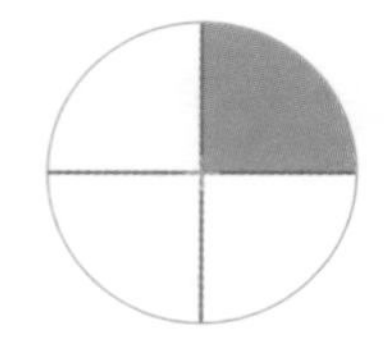

d

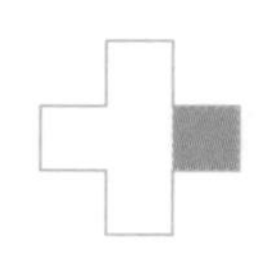

1 mark each

Note to Parent

Parts **a** and **b** are straight forward, being drawn on a square grid (there are alternative answers for **a** and **b** – three squares should be shaded) but they require recognition that ⅛ of 24 is 3 or ⅓ of 9 is 3.

Total 4 marks

38

money	frequency	total
0–19p		0
20–39p		0
40–59p	II	2
60–79p	III	3
80–99p	II	2
£1.00–£1.19	I	1
£1.20–£1.39	II	2
£1.40–£1.59	III	3
£1.60–£1.79	II	2

Award one mark for each correct total — *9 marks*

Note to Parent

Check that the totals agree with your child's tallying. The ability to group information into equal width bands is a useful skill. If your child hasn't met this yet at school, talk through it with him or her.

Total 9 marks

39
- a August — *1 mark*
- b Good answers would identify good weather, or school holidays, or family holidays. — *1 mark*
- c £900 — *1 mark*
- d Good answers would identify special Christmas treats, events or holidays, or enjoying a snowy landscape — *1 mark*

Note to Parent

Children need to be able to draw reasonable conclusions from simple graphs.

Total 4 marks

40 4, 3 — *2 marks*

Note to Parent

Your child will need to plot each route, making sure she or he uses the horizontal number first and the vertical one second. There is only one possible answer.

Total 2 marks

MARKING GRID

LEVEL 2 *Pages 1–8*

Question	Marks available	Marks scored
1	3	
2	5	
3	4	
4	4	
5	2	
6	5	
7	4	
8	5	
9	2	
10	2	
Total	**36**	

LEVEL 3 *Pages 9–21*

Question	Marks available	Marks scored
11	3	
12	4	
13	1	
14	5	
15	4	
16	3	
17	6	
18	3	
19	2	
20	2	
21	2	
22	3	
23	4	
24	8	
25	5	
Total	**55**	

LEVEL 4 *Pages 22–35*

Question	Marks available	Marks scored
26	10	
27	4	
28	6	
29	2	
30	5	
31	2	
32	5	
33	3	
34	4	
35	3	
36	3	
37	4	
38	9	
39	4	
40	2	
Total	**66**	